To parents and teachers

We hope you and the children will enjoy reading this story in either English or Spanish. The story is simple, but not *simplified* so the language of the Spanish and the English is quite natural but there is lots of repetition.

At the back of the book is a small picture dictionary with the key words and how to pronounce them. There is also a simple pronunciation guide to the whole story on the last page

Here are a few suggestions on using the book:

• Read the story aloud in English first, to get to know it. Treat it like any other picture book: look at the pictures, talk about the story and the characters and so on.

• Then look at the picture dictionary and say the Spanish names for the key words. Ask the children to repeat them. Concentrate on speaking the words out loud, rather than reading them.

• Go back and read the story again, this time in English *and* Spanish. Don't worry if your pronunciation isn't quite correct. Just have fun trying it out. Check the guide at the back of the book, if necessary, but you'll soon pick up how to say the Spanish words.

• When you think you and the children are ready, you can try reading the story in Spanish only. Ask the children to say it with you. Only ask them to read it if they are keen to try. The spelling could be confusing and put them off.

• Above all encourage the children to have a go and give lots of praise. Little children are usually quite unselfconscious and this is excellent for building up confidence in a foreign language.

Published by b small publishing ltd
The Book Shed, 36 Leyborne Park, Kew, Richmond, Surrey, TW9 3HA
www.bsmall.co.uk
Text © b small publishing, 1996   Illustrations © Alex de Wolf, 1996
1 2 3 4 5
All rights reserved.
Design: *Lone Morton*   Editorial: *Catherine Bruzzone*   Production: *Madeleine Ehm*
Printed in China by WKT Co. Ltd.
ISBN 978-1-905710-81-2 (paperback with spine)
British Library Cataloguing in Publication Data. A catalogue record for this book is available from the British Library.

I want my banana!

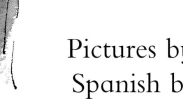

¡Quiero mi plátano!

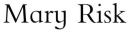

Mary Risk

Pictures by Alex de Wolf
Spanish by Rosa Martín

b small publishing

Monkey has lost his banana.

El mono ha perdido su plátano.

He's sad

Está triste.

"Would you like an orange?"
says Python.

"¿Quieres una naranja?"
dice la Pitón.

"It's nice and juicy."

"Es buena y jugosa".

"No thanks," says Monkey.

"No, gracias", dice el Mono.

"I want my banana."

"Quiero mi plátano".

"Have some nuts," says Parrot.

"Toma unas nueces", dice el Loro.

"They're delicious."

"Son deliciosas".

"No, thanks," says Monkey.

"No, gracias", dice el Mono.

"I only like bananas."

"Sólo me gustan los plátanos".

"Have a pineapple," says Hyena.

"Toma una piña"; dice la Hiena.

"It's very sweet."

"Es muy dulce".

"No, thanks," says Monkey.

"No, gracias", dice el Mono.

"I just want my banana."

"Sólo quiero mi plátano".

"Come here, little Monkey,"
says Tiger.

"Ven aquí, Monito", dice el Tigre.

"I'll give you your banana."

"Yo te daré tu plátano".

But Monkey sees his banana.

Pero el Mono ve su plátano.

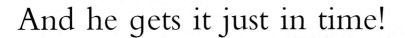

And he gets it just in time!

¡Y lo coge justo a tiempo!

Monkey's happy now.

El Mono está contento ahora.

"Bananas are best," he says.

"Los plátanos son lo mejor", dice.

Pronouncing Spanish

Don't worry if your pronunciation isn't quite correct. The important thing is to be willing to try. The pronunciation guide here is based on the Spanish accent used in Spain. Although it cannot be completely accurate, it certainly will be a great help:

• Read the guide as naturally as possible, as if it were English.

• Put stress on the letters in *italics* e.g. past*el*.

If you can, ask a Spanish speaking person to help and move on as soon as possible to speaking the words without the guide.

Note: Spanish adjectives usually have two forms, one for masculine and one for feminine nouns. They often look very similar but are pronounced slightly differently, e.g., **jugoso** and **jugosa** (see the word list below).

Words Las palabras

lass pal-*abrass*

monkey
el mono

el *mono*

python
la pitón

lah pee*ton*

parrot
el loro
el *lo*ro

hyena
la hiena
lah ee*yen*a

tiger
el tigre
el *tee*greh

banana
el plátano
el *plat*-ano

orange
la naranja
lah na*ran*-ha

nuts
las nueces
lass noo-*eh*-thess

pineapple
la piña
lah *peen*-ya

sad

triste

*treess*teh

sweet

dulce

dool-theh

happy

contento/contenta

*conten*to/*conten*ta

juicy

jugoso/jugosa

hoo-*go*-zo/hoo-*go*-za

would you like a...?

¿quieres un/una...?

kee-*airess* oon/*oo*na...?

nice

bueno/buena

boo-*eh*-no/boo-*eh*-na

have a...

toma un/una...

toma oon/*oo*na...

delicious

delicioso/deliciosa

dellee-thee-*o*-zo/dellee-thee-*o*-za

I want a...

quiero un/una...

kee-*airo* oon/*oo*na

A simple guide to pronouncing this Spanish story

El mono ha perdido su plátano.
el *mono* a pair*dee*-do soo *plat*-ano

Está triste.
est*ah* *tree*steh

"¿Quieres una naranja?"
kee-*airess* *oo*na na*ran*-ha

dice la Pitón.
*dee*theh lah pee*ton*

"Es buena y jugosa".
ess boo-*eh*-na ee hoo-*go*-za

"No, gracias", dice el Mono.
noh, *grath*-ee-ass, *dee*sseh el *mono*

"Quiero mi plátano".
kee-*airo* mee *plat*-ano

"Toma unas nueces", dice el Loro.
toma *oo*nass noo-*eh*-thess, *dee*sseh el *loro*

"Son deliciosas".
son dell-eethee-*o*-zass

"No, gracias", dice el Mono.
noh, *grath*-ee-ass, *dee*theh el *mono*

"Sólo me gustan los plátanos".
solo meh *goo*stan loss *plat*-anoss

"Toma una piña", dice la Hiena.
toma *oo*na *peen*ya, *dee*theh lah ee*yen*a

"Es muy dulce".
ess mwee *dool*-theh

"No, gracias", dice el Mono.
noh, *gras*-ee-ass, *dee*theh el *mono*

"Sólo quiero mi plátano".
solo kee-*airo* mee *plat*-ano

"Ven aquí, Monito", dice el Tigre.
ven a*kee*, monee-to, *dee*theh el *tee*greh.

"Yo te daré tu plátano"
yoh teh da-*reh* too *plat*-ano

Pero el Mono ve su plátano.
pair-o el *mono* beh soo *plat*-ano

¡Y lo coge justo a tiempo!
ee lo *co*-heh *hoo*sto a tee-*empo*

El Mono está contento ahora.
el *mono* est*ah* con*tento* a-*ora*

"Los plátanos son lo mejor", dice.
loss *plat*-anoss son loh meh-hor, *dee*theh